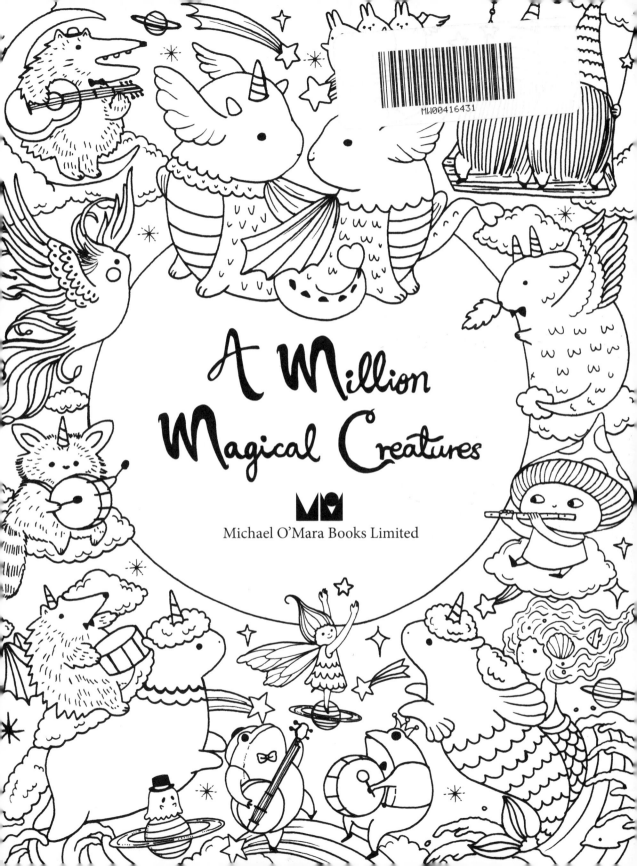

A Million Magical Creatures

Michael O'Mara Books Limited

First published in Great Britain in 2021 by Michael O'Mara Books Limited,
9 Lion Yard, Tremadoc Road, London SW4 7NQ

W   www.mombooks.com
f   Michael O'Mara Books
y   @OMaraBooks
O   @omarabooks

A CIP catalogue record for this book is available from the British Library.

ISBN: 978-1-78929-353-1

2 4 6 8 10 9 7 5 3 1

This book was printed in China.

MIX
Paper from
responsible sources
FSC
www.fsc.org
FSC® C010256

Illustrated by

Lulu Mayo

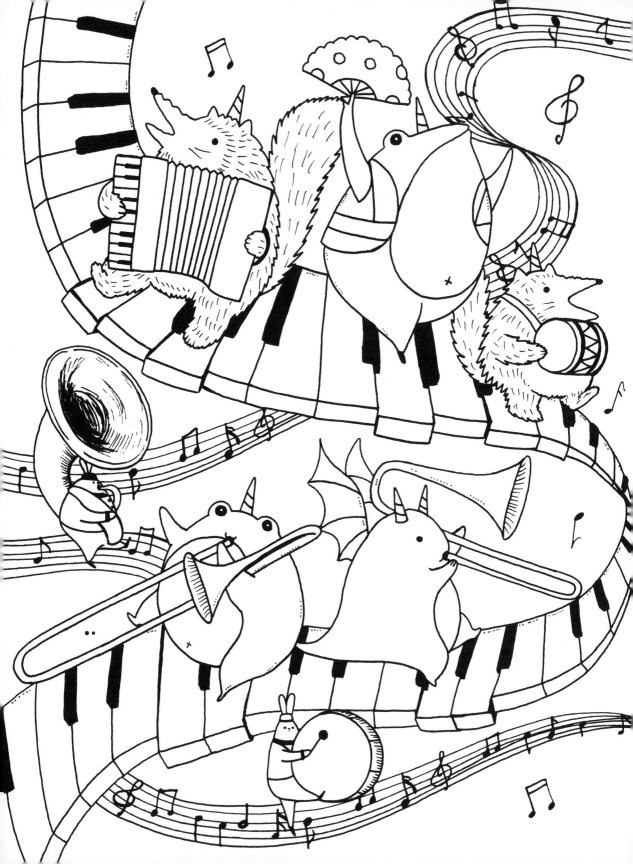